D0653046

To Calla, two years hence
A.B.

For Caitlin
J.L.

First published 1998 by Walker Books Ltd
87 Vauxhall Walk, London SE11 5HJ

2 4 6 8 10 9 7 5 3

Text © 1998 Alison Boyle
Illustrations © 1998 Julie Lacome

This book has been typeset in Gill Sans Bold Educational.

Printed in Singapore

British Library Cataloguing in Publication Data
A catalogue record for this book is
available from the British Library.

ISBN 0-7445-4922-1

Where is Little Croc?

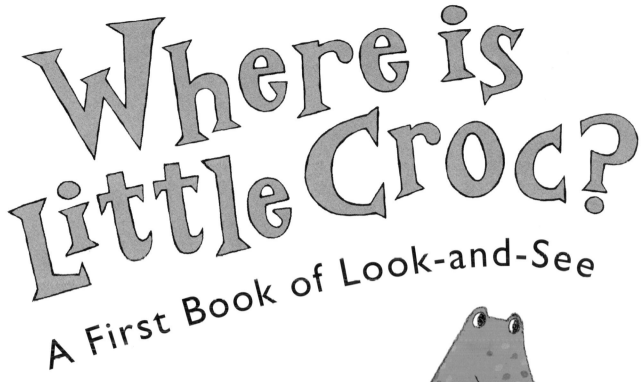

A First Book of Look-and-See

Alison Boyle

Illustrated by
Julie Lacome

WALKER BOOKS

AND SUBSIDIARIES

LONDON • BOSTON • SYDNEY

Mum was getting Little Croc's bath ready.

But Little Croc wasn't ready for his bath. He had a better idea.

Little Croc hid in the living room.

Can you find Little Croc?
And can you find Muncher?

Little Croc hid in the kitchen.

Where are you, Little Croc?

Can you find Little Croc?
And can you find Swish?

Little Croc hid in the playroom.

Can you find Little Croc?
And can you find Spiky?

Little Croc hid on the landing.

Can you find Little Croc?
And can you find Grin?

Little Croc hid in the bedroom.

Where are you,
Little Croc?

Can you find Little Croc?
And can you find Monster?

At bedtime, Little Croc hid again.

Can you spot Little Croc and all his toys?